Christmas Songs

Illustrated by
Miriam Latimer, Simona Sanfilippo,
Nicola Evans, Giuditta Gaviraghi and Alik Arzoumanian

Acknowledgements:

The publishers would like to acknowledge with thanks permission to use the following copyright material:

Santa Claus is comin' to town: Words and music by Coots, J Fred/Gillespie, Haven; ©1934 EMI Catalogue Partnership; Worldwide print rights controlled by Warner Bros Inc, USA/IMP Ltd; Reproduced by permission of IMP Ltd.

Let it snow! Let it snow! Let it snow!: Words by Sammy Cahn; Music by Jule Styne; ©1945 Cahn music Corp, USA; Chappell Morris Ltd, London, W6 8BS; Reproduced by permission of IMP Ltd and Hal Leonard Corp.

Rudolph the red-nosed reindeer: Words and music by Johnny Marks; ©1949 St Nicholas Music Inc, USA; Warner/Chappell Music Ltd, London W6 8BS; Reproduced by permission of IMP Ltd.

Winter wonderland: Music by Bernard, Felix; Words by Smith, Richard B; ©1934 Bregman Vocco & Conn Inc; Francis Day & Hunter Ltd, London WC2H 0EA; Redwood Music Ltd, London NW1 8BD; Reproduced by permission of IMP Ltd.

I wish it could be Christmas every day: © 1973 Roy Wood.

I saw Mommy kissing Santa Claus: ©1952 Jewell Music Inc, by kind permission of Blue Ribbon Music Ltd.

The Christmas Song (Chestnuts roasting on an open fire): Words and music by Mel Torme/Robert Wells; ©1946 & 1988 Edwin H Morris & Co Inc, USA; Chappell Morris, London, W6 8BS; Reproduced by permission of IMP Ltd and Hal Leonard Corp.

A catalogue record for this book is available from the British Library

Published by Ladybird Books Ltd
80 Strand, London, WC2R 0RL
A Penguin Company

2 4 6 8 10 9 7 5 3
© Ladybird Books Ltd MMIX
LADYBIRD and the device of a Ladybird are trademarks of Ladybird Books Ltd

ISBN: 978-1-40930-179-0

Printed in China

Contents

Jingle bells

Dashing through the snow
In a one-horse open sleigh,
O'er the fields we go,
Laughing all the way.
Bells on bob-tail ring,
Making spirits bright.
What fun it is to ride and sing
a sleighing song tonight.

Jingle bells, jingle bells,
jingle all the way.
Oh, what fun it is to ride
in a one-horse open sleigh.
Jingle bells, jingle bells,
jingle all the way.
Oh, what fun it is to ride
in a one-horse open sleigh.

Santa Claus is comin' to town

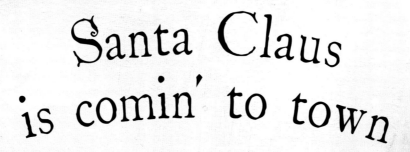

You better watch out, you better not cry,
Better not pout, I'm telling you why:
Santa Claus is comin' to town.

He's making a list and checking it twice,
Gonna find out who's naughty and nice:
Santa Claus is comin' to town.

He sees you when you're sleepin',
He knows when you're awake,
He knows if you've been bad or good,
So be good for goodness sake.

You better watch out, you better not cry,
Better not pout, I'm telling you why,
Santa Claus is comin' to town.

Let it snow! Let it snow! Let it snow!

Oh the weather outside is frightful
But the fire is so delightful,
And since we've no place to go,
Let it snow! Let it snow! Let it snow!

It doesn't show signs of stopping
And I brought some corn for popping,
The lights are turned way down low,
Let it snow! Let it snow! Let it snow!

When we finally kiss goodnight,
How I'll hate going out in the storm!
But if you'll really hold me tight,
All the way home I'll be warm.

The fire is slowly dying
And my dear we're still goodbyeing,
But as long as you love me so,
Let it snow! Let it snow! Let it snow!

Rudolph the red-nosed reindeer

You know Dasher and Dancer and Prancer and Vixen,
Comet and Cupid and Donner and Blitzen,
But do you recall the most famous reindeer of all?

Rudolph the red-nosed reindeer
had a very shiny nose,
And if you ever saw it,
you would even say it glows.
All of the other reindeer
used to laugh and call him names,
They never let poor Rudolph
join in any reindeer games.

Then one foggy Christmas Eve,
Santa came to say,
"Rudolph, with your nose so bright,
won't you guide my sleigh tonight?"
Then how the reindeer loved him
as they shouted out with glee:
"Rudolph the red-nosed reindeer,
you'll go down in history!"

We wish you a merry Christmas

We wish you a merry Christmas,
We wish you a merry Christmas,
We wish you a merry Christmas
and a happy New Year!

Good tidings we bring
For you and your kin,
We wish you a merry Christmas
and a happy New Year!

Now bring us some figgy pudding,
Now bring us some figgy pudding,
Now bring us some figgy pudding,
Now bring some to us here.

Good tidings we bring
For you and your kin,
We wish you a merry Christmas
and a happy New Year!

We won't go until we get it,
We won't go until we get it,
We won't go until we get it,
So bring some right here!

Good tidings we bring
For you and your kin,
We wish you a merry Christmas
and a happy New Year!

We all like a figgy pudding,
We all like a figgy pudding,
So bring us some figgy pudding,
With all its good cheer!

Good tidings we bring
For you and your kin,
We wish you a merry Christmas
and a happy New Year!

Winter wonderland

Sleigh bells ring, are you list'nin'?
In the lane snow is glist'nin',
A beautiful sight,
We're happy tonight,
Walkin' in a winter wonderland!

Gone away is the bluebird,
Here to stay is a new bird,
He sings a love song,
As we go along,
Walkin' in a winter wonderland!

In the meadow we can build a snowman,
Then pretend that he is Parson Brown.
He'll say, "Are you married?"
We'll say, "No, man!
But you can do the job when you're in town!"

Later on we'll conspire
As we dream by the fire
To face unafraid the plans that we made,
Walkin' in a winter wonderland!

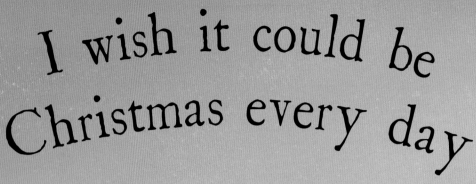

I wish it could be Christmas every day

Oh when the snowman brings the snow,
Oh well he just might like to know
He's put a great big smile on somebody's face.
If you jump into your bed,
Quickly cover up your head,
Don't you lock the doors,
You know that sweet Santa Claus is on the way.

Oh I wish it could be Christmas ev'ry day.
When the kids start singing
and the band begins to play.
Oh I wish it could be Christmas ev'ry day,
So let the bells ring out for Christmas.

I saw Mommy kissing Santa Claus

I saw Mommy kissing Santa Claus
Underneath the mistletoe last night;
She didn't see me creep down the stairs
to have a peep,
She thought that I was tucked up in
my bedroom fast asleep.
Then I saw Mommy tickle Santa Claus
Underneath his beard so snowy white;
Oh, what a laugh it would have been
If Daddy had only seen
Mommy kissing Santa Claus last night.

The twelve days
of Christmas

On the first day of Christmas
my true love sent to me,
a partridge in a pear tree.

On the second day of Christmas
my true love sent to me,
two turtledoves
and a partridge in a pear tree.

On the third day of Christmas
my true love sent to me,
three French hens,
two turtledoves
and a partridge in a pear tree.

On the fourth day of Christmas
my true love sent to me,
four calling birds,
three French hens...

On the fifth day of Christmas
my true love sent to me,
five gold rings,
four calling birds...

On the sixth day of Christmas
my true love sent to me,
six geese a-laying,
five gold rings...

On the seventh day of Christmas
my true love sent to me,
seven swans a-swimming,
six geese a-laying...

On the eighth day of Christmas
my true love sent to me,
eight maids a-milking,
seven swans a-swimming...

On the ninth day of Christmas
my true love sent to me,
nine ladies dancing,
eight maids a-milking...

On the tenth day of Christmas
my true love sent to me,
ten lords a-leaping,
nine ladies dancing...

On the eleventh day of Christmas
my true love sent to me,
eleven pipers piping,
ten lords a-leaping...

On the twelfth day of Christmas
my true love sent to me,
twelve drummers drumming,
eleven pipers piping,
ten lords a-leaping,
nine ladies dancing,
eight maids a-milking,
seven swans a-swimming,
six geese a-laying,
five gold rings,
four calling birds,
three French hens,
two turtledoves
and a partridge in a pear tree!

The Christmas song

Chestnuts roasting on an open fire,
Jack Frost nipping at your nose,
Yuletide carols being sung by a choir
And folks dressed up like Eskimos.
Ev'rybody knows a turkey and some mistletoe
Help to make the season bright.
Tiny tots with their eyes all aglow
Will find it hard to sleep tonight.

They know that Santa's on his way;
He's loaded lots of toys and goodies
on his sleigh
And ev'ry mother's child is gonna spy
To see if reindeer really know how to fly.
And so, I'm offering this simple phrase
To kids from one to ninety-two.
Altho' it's been said many times, many ways:
"Merry Christmas to you."